ROADWORKS

For Alice – why should the boys have all the fun? SS
For Jackie and Harry BL

First published 2008
by Walker Books Ltd
87 Vauxhall Walk, London SE11 5HJ

This edition published 2011

10 9 8 7 6 5 4 3 2 1

Text © 2008 Sally Sutton
Illustrations © 2008 Brian Lovelock

The right of Sally Sutton and Brian Lovelock to be identified as author
and illustrator respectively of this work has been asserted by them in
accordance with the Copyright, Designs and Patents Act 1988

This book has been typeset in Franklin Gothic Extra Condensed

Printed in China

British Library Cataloguing in Publication Data:
a catalogue record for this book is available
from the British Library

ISBN 978-1-4063-2537-9

www.walker.co.uk

ROADWORKS

SALLY SUTTON · ILLUSTRATED BY BRIAN LOVELOCK

WALKER BOOKS
AND SUBSIDIARIES
LONDON · BOSTON · SYDNEY · AUCKLAND

Plan the road. Plan the road.

Mark it on the map.

Hammer in the marking pegs.

Ping! BANG! TAP!

Move the earth. Move the earth.

Dig and cut and push.

Clear a pathway for the road.

Screech! BOOM! WHOOSH!

Load the dirt. Load the dirt.

Scoop and swing and drop.

Slam it down into the truck.

Bump!

WHUMP!

WHOP!

Tip the stones. Tip the stones.

Lift and slide and dump.

Lay the groundwork for the road.

Crash! ROAR!

THUMP!

Pack the ground. Pack the ground.

Roll one way, then back.

Make the roadbed good and hard.

Clang! CRUNCH!
CRACK!

Seal the road. Seal the road.

Make it hot and squishy.

Spread the sticky tar and stones.

Sploshy! SPLASHY! SPLISHY!

Roll the tar. Roll the tar.

Make it firm and flat.

Squash it down and press it out.

Squelch! SPLUCK! SPLAT!

Stop the work. Stop the work.

Time to break for lunch.

Sandwiches and drinks and fruit.

Mark the road. Mark the road.

Give the paint a squirt.

Paint the lines in nice and straight.

Whizz! SPLOP! SPLURT!

Raise the signs. Raise the signs.

Drag and hoist and ram.

Force them down into their holes.

Thwack! WHOP! WHAM!

Light the road. Light the road.

No one wants a crash.

Test the lights and see them shine.

Flick! FLACK! FLASH!

Plant the trees. Plant the trees.

Dig and stamp and lug.

Water them to help them grow.

Drip! DROP! GLUG!

Tidy up. Tidy up.

Lift and load and sweep.

Drive away those big machines.

Swish! cHuG!

BEEP!

Shout hooray! The work is done.

Ready, now? Let's zoom.

Drive along your brand-new road.

MACHINE FACTS

EXCAVATOR: The excavator uses a large scoop to dig the ground. The cabin where the driver sits can swing around to face in any direction.

BULLDOZER: A bulldozer has a blade at the front for clearing and levelling the ground.

FRONT-END LOADER: A front-end loader has a scoop at the front. It lifts and moves things.

DUMP TRUCK: The dump truck has a tray at the back. It can tilt up to dump out dirt and rocks.

ROAD-ROLLER: A road-roller flattens the road to make it hard. Its roller is called a 'drum'.

GRADER: A grader uses its blade to make the ground very flat so the asphalt on top will be even and smooth.

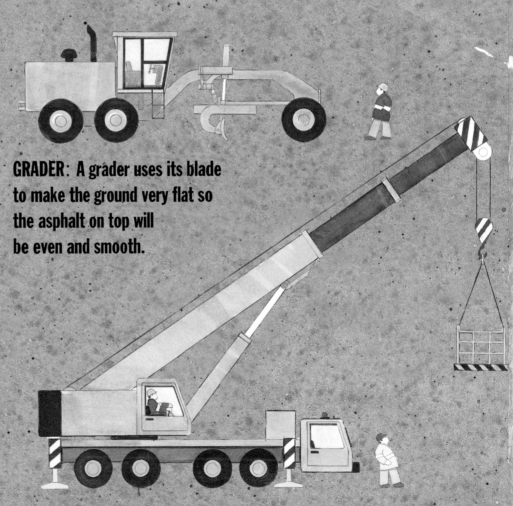

TRUCK-MOUNTED CRANE: This crane uses its hook to lift equipment. It has wire cables that wind up and down.